So what should you be zapping in the Annual?

Try It Now!

Wherever you see the interactive icon you'll be able to unlock a fun experience to enjoy on your device. There are nine scattered throughout the Annual and one on the front cover to discover. See if you can find them all.

ZAP NOW!

Ready
Open Zappar on your device.

Aim
Scan the code on the page.

Zap
Then point your device at the page and watch it come to life!

A few helpful tips...

To get the best possible experience here are a few hints and tips:

- Connect to wifi if you can and the experiences will download even quicker than on 3G.
- Try and keep the pages as flat as you can for the best effect. Rest the Annual on a table or on the floor.
- Try and keep the full page in view from your phone after scanning the code. Don't get too close or far away if you can help it.

- Try and keep the pages clean and free from tears, pen and other marks as this may affect the experience.
- It's best to view the pages in good lighting conditions if you can.

If you're still having problems then do contact us at support@zappar.com and we'll do our best to help you.

CONTENTS

Pedigree®

Published 2014. Pedigree Books Limited, Beech Hill House,
Walnut Gardens, Exeter, Devon EX4 4DH.
www.pedigreebooks.com — books@pedigreegroup.co.uk
The Pedigree trademark, email and website addresses, are the sole
and exclusive properties of Pedigree Group Limited, used under
licence in this publication.

Welcome, fellow explorers, to the exciting and dangerous world of Temple Run. I'm Guy Dangerous, the number one adventurer! When I'm not searching for lost treasure, swinging on vines through forgotten jungles, jumping fallen obstacles and running along narrow crumbling precipices from those terrifying demon monkeys, well... I'm planning my next thrilling adventure. And making sure I always have my handy ruck sack!

You know the score - enter the Temple, grab the idol and RUN! So, have you got what it takes to join me and my intrepid explorer pals in an awesome Temple Run adventure? Pack your ruck sack (more later on what to take) and turn the page to start your mission. Complete all the activities along the way and make sure you collect as many gems, coins, artifacts, power ups and abilities as you can. Record everything you pick up, on your quest score card at the end of this Annual. Good luck, be brave and keep your wits about you. Oh, and don't forget to count up how many 'running explorers' you see dashing through this book.

Okay, gotta RUN now... that screeching and those scrapping claws are getting very close...!

GUY DANGEROUS

#1 TEMPLE RUN

UNLOCK:
Start playing the game

ABILITIES:
· Super fit
· Distance running at high speeds
· Swinging on vines

DISLIKES:
· Demon Monkeys
· Rapids
· Narrow clifftop walkways

POWER UP:
· Protective shield

Good luck, be brave and keep your wits about you. Oh, and don't forget to count up how many 'running explorers' you see dashing through this book!

TANGLED VINE TEASER!

Our intrepid explorer, Guy Dangerous, has been swinging on so many vines through the jungle, trying to find the lost temple and the golden idol, that he's got his khaki breeches all in a twist! Help him untangle himself to see which vine he should swing on to reach his goal.

ZAP NOW!

if you succeed in untwisting guy's tangles! COLLECT **50 GEMS**

HOW TO DRAW NO.1 EXPLORER GUY DANGEROUS!

Follow these simple steps and learn how to draw this speedy Temple Run hero.

STEP 1
Using a pencil lightly draw simple shapes to construct Guys pose. It is important to press light with your pencil at this stage.

STEP 2
Draw Guy's hair, facial features and outline now.

STEP 3
Gradually add the details of Guys clothes bag and boots.

STEP 4
Use colours and sharp pencil lines to complete your drawing of Guy Dangerous.

AWESOME! WELL DONE EXPLORER YOUR MISSION IS COMPLETE!

if you can complete a drawing of the speedy hero!

COLLECT 50 GEMS

GUY'S TOP TIPS FOR INTREPID EXPLORERS

We talked to Guy Dangerous to get a few handy hints — well who better than this ace adventurer to give us his top tips. Guy Dangerous has been in the exploration business for a few years now, so he's had plenty of experience, but he did tell us that when he first started out, he was a bit 'green' and made quite a few mistakes along the way. The important thing, he said, was to always stick to your goal, be prepared for the unexpected, and NEVER, EVER give up!

A good explorer should be:

Fit (you've got a lot of running to do!)
Strong
Agile
Brave
Curious
Enthusiastic
Resourceful
Resilient
Quick-witted
Keen Sensed
Calm in a crisis
Instinctive
Determined
Able to survive in the wild
In touch with nature

If you can, before you set out on a quest, brush up on your navigation skills — reading maps, understanding the coordinates and grid references, and using a compass.

A can-do attitude and a bit of charm can go a long way on an adventure, too! It is important to take the right equipment with you too. You don't want to be laden down with too much stuff, because you've got a lot of running and trekking to do over long distances. A medium-sized ruck sack is ideal. When it's full you should still be able to lift it and carry it on your back. As you're going to be travelling and running around all sorts of terrains, wear a sturdy pair of walking boots, and long trousers to protect your legs (insects, reeds, branches, foliage etc.).

Basic survival skills in the wild are also a must for any would-be adventurer – know how to build and light a fire, how to make a simple shelter, and how to tell which wild fruits, berries and mushrooms you can or can't eat.

These simple skills could save your life (ask Montana Smith – he is an expert in this field!).

A good piece of advice Guy gave us was to watch out for booby traps – trip-wire vines, leaves and branches covering a hole in the ground and animal snares. And when you're in a temple, ALWAYS think before you start pressing on bricks or symbols on the walls, otherwise you might just find yourself plummeting down a tunnel into a creepy tomb (Guy D learnt the hard way!).

Here's a checklist of some handy things to pack:

- ☐ Water
- ☐ Tinned food that doesn't need cooking (don't forget your tin opener, otherwise you might go hungry!)
- ☐ Fresh fruit for the start of your journey
- ☐ Matches (for lighting a fire)
- ☐ Torch (a must-have if you find yourself in a mine shaft or dark cavern)
- ☐ Insect repellant
- ☐ A map of the area you are exploring
- ☐ A compass
- ☐ A multi-purpose Swiss army knife
- ☐ A small digging tool (for finding buried treasure!)
- ☐ A sleeping bag
- ☐ A small leather pouch to stash any coins and gems you collect
- ☐ One small luxury item (Guy says he doesn't go anywhere without his hair gel!)

Guy's final word to us was on what to do if you encounter the scary Demon Monkey (remember, a good explorer must be prepared for the unexpected and be able to think his way out of a dangerous situation) …

RUN! AND DON'T LOOK BACK!

ANCIENT TEMPLE BLUEPRINT

It's dark and creepy, with strange shadows dancing on the moss-covered crumbling walls. The air is damp and musty in the maze of closed-in chambers inside this ancient monument. Eerie noises make you jump, but you've got to keep going and find the hidden idol before anyone else gets it, or some scary creature gets you!

For designing your own temple
COLLECT
20 COINS

DESIGN A BLUEPRINT MAP OF YOUR OWN ANCIENT TEMPLE WITH SECRET CHAMBERS AND TUNNELS, CREEPY STATUES, AND OBSTACLES!

A B C D E F G H I J K L M N O P Q R S T U V W X Y Z AA AB AC AD AE AF AG AH

1 2 3 4 5 6 7 8 9 10 11 12 13 14 15 16 17 18 19 20 21 22 23 24 25 26 27 28 29 30 31 32 33 34 35

SECRET TEMPLE CODE

You found the precious idol, but not without a few adventures on the way! Write a secret coded message to leave clues for your fellow explorers to locate the idol in your temple on the previous page. Make up your own hieroglyphic symbols for each letter of the alphabet. Let's hope it doesn't fall into the wrong hands!

a   b   c   d   e   f   g   h   i

j   k   l   m   n   o   p   q   r

s   t   u   v   w   x   y   z

Secret Coded Message

....

....

....

if you make a Top Secret Code COLLECT **10 GEMS**

My Ancient Idol

MEET KARMA LEE

I came across Karma Lee when Scarlett and I were trapped in an ancient temple. She was also trying to find a way out, and seemed pretty desperate to take the golden idol with her. I could tell Scarlett was not that keen on her, and to be honest, my first impression of her was that she was one smart, calculating lady, but very cold and just out for herself. You definitely would not want her as your opponent.

As I've got to know her a bit better, I've realized that my first impressions were wrong. Karma is a private person, but she is actually really generous, and she would use her impressive martial art skills and intelligence to help you out of a dangerous situation, even if it put her in danger too.

Notes:

Heiress of greatest dynasty of the 22nd century,

Scholar

Cultured

KARMA LEE

#2 TEMPLE RUN

UNLOCK:
Collect 25,000 coins

ABILITIES:
· Impressive intellect
· Skilled in martial arts
· Experienced world traveller

DISLIKES:
· Snakes and Crocodiles
· Cheaters and liars
· Bad losers

POWER UP:
· Score bonus – collect an instant 500 point bonus

ARE YOU KARMA SMART?

You're obviously a great adventurer, having already worked your way through the activities in this Annual up to here, but are you up to the challenge of taking on the mighty brainpower of Karma Lee? This incredible lady is one smart cookie!

if you're as smart as Karma!

COLLECT

25,000 COINS

Don't look up the answers though, because Karma hates cheaters, and she might just have to try out some of her impressive martial art moves on you – you've been warned!

1. Karma Lee left the temple at 7.35am. It took her 27 minutes to run to the rapids. What time did she arrive there?

2. Guy Dangerous collected 420 coins and 167 gems on his latest quest. Unfortunately, he lost 173 coins and 32 gems running away from a demon monkey. How many coins and gems has Guy got left?

3. Zack Wonder collected 63 artifacts. He wants to share them with the 6 other explorers. How many artifacts will each explorer get?

4. Montana Smith says he will sell you the idol he has found for 1,333 coins. You only have 864 coins. How many more coins do you need to collect?

5. Francisco Montoya says he will give you 20% of his gems if you help him find the lost temple. He has 500 gems. How many will he give you?

EXPLORER WORDSEARCH

When it comes to intelligence, Karma Lee is head and shoulders above everyone else! She is definitely a worthy ally, especially when it comes to cracking codes and solving clues. Go head to head with this super smart explorer by trying out this tricky Temple Run wordsearch and crossword puzzle. She remains an undefeated champion; can you be the first to beat her?

```
Y K A R M A L E E S L F R
D E P T G H R Q H Z O Y U
G A K F E U G I P O D D N
B S X N S M E L P Y I T N
K J Y A O L P B V F N F E
E H E U D M W L I O E C R
Y R M G M K N J E Y D T A
T S N I O C Q O D M L Z K
Y U C E Q D S B M O O R L
C X W P Q L W M Z E G Q I
W K R O K G R E E Y D W R
X V E X V K Q E L G T H H
P O O L E T I N I F N I X
```

TEMPLE	RUNNER	INFINITE
DEMON MONKEY	GOLDEN IDOL	LOOP
COINS	TREASURE	SHIELD
GEMS	KARMA LEE	

KARMA'S CRYPTIC CROSSWORD

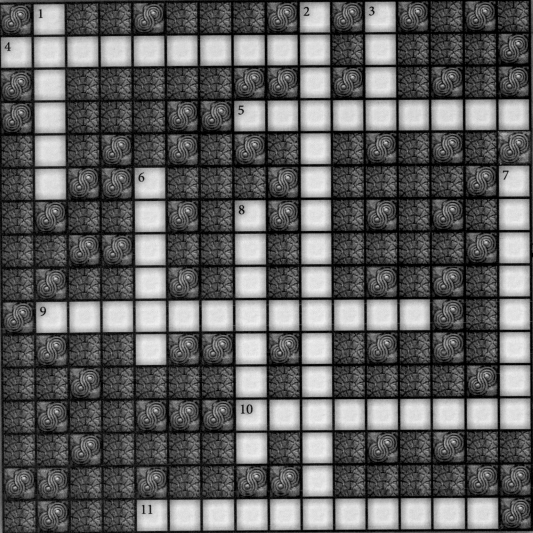

Across

4. What was Zack Wonder before he became a swift-footed explorer?

5. An explorer will need a torch if he finds himself climbing into this dark cavernous place to search for the idol.

9. Wanted in the Wild West, this quiet treasure seeker can often be found drinking alone in saloon bars.

10. As a bonus for completing levels, explorers can also find other ancient treasures on their adventure. What is the name for these collectables?

11. Karma Lee is an expert in which ancient fighting skill?

Down

1. What type of creature is the demonic monster that loves to chase (and eat!) explorers?

2. He might be a smooth talker, but this armour-clad explorer is a crafty thief.

3. All that glitters is not gold in Temple Run. What other sparkling objects do all explorers need to collect on their quest?

6. Although he doesn't like to admit to it, Barry Bones likes to have a supply of these when he sets off on a new adventure.

7. When the power meter is glowing green, what can an explorer activate to help.

8. Which razor-sharp toothed creatures does the normally fearless Scarlett really dislike?

if you complete the crossword

COLLECT INFINTY LOOP & SHIELD POWER UP

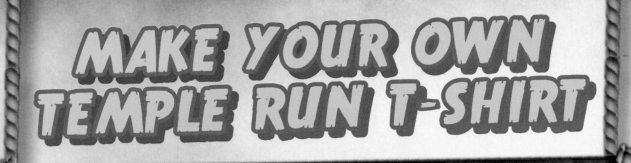

MAKE YOUR OWN TEMPLE RUN T-SHIRT

Will you be running with our hero explorers, or clawing and screeching your way over to the dark demonic side? Choose your path wisely before you start your next adventure, and then collect everything you'll need to design your own awesome Temple Run T-shirt. Rockin', dude!

1. Trace, photocopy or scan the two designs on the opposite page.

2. Choose the design you want to stencil onto your T-shirt (if you make the wrong choice you've only got yourself to blame! You've been warned!).

3. Tape or glue your stencil onto thick card to make the stencil strong.

4. Carefully cut out all the black areas to make the stencil holes.

5. Attach your stencil to the front of your T-shirt with masking tape.

6. Choose the colour of fabirc paint you want to use. Paint through the stencil onto your T-shirt, making sure you cover all the holes. If you choose the monkey desing, you will need to hold the nose shapes in position and paint around them.

7. Gently peel away the stencil. Allow the paint to dry.

8. Some fabric paints need 'fixing' with an iron. Follow the instructions carefully for your paint. Make sure you cover the painted area with a cloth first, to stop it sticking to the iron.

9. Once the paint is dry or 'fixed', your awesome Temple Run-shirt is ready to wear with pride!

KEEP ON
RUNNING!

FEEDING
TIME!

FOREST ADVENTURE MAZE

Guy Dangerous has taken a wrong turn. He's got lost in the forest after nearly being caught by a screeching demon monkey. Help Guy get back on track (he really wants that idol), avoiding obstacles, dead ends and other generally perilous things like cliff-tops, rapids and dark caverns! He must reach the temple before dark to collect more coins and gems, and to avoid running into any more hungry monkeys! Come on Guy, RUN dude!

LUCKY ESCAPE! THAT WAS TOO CLOSE FOR COMFORT!

FEEDING TIME!

if you help Guy reach the Idol COLLECT 100 GEMS

ANCIENT SYMBOLS MYSTERY

Karma Lee has stumbled across these ancient symbols carved into the temple wall. Some are worn away or covered in moss. Perhaps they're a clue to where a golden idol is hidden? Help her fill in the missing symbols in each row so she can achieve her treasure hunter objective and collect 50,000 points.

Barry is a great guy to have along on a quest. He wasn't born to a life of adventure like me, but his years of fighting crime in the city have given him the finest explorer skills to cope with the dangers and unexpected events that always crop up on every quest journey. He's logical (a great skill to have when you're in a tight spot!) and keeps his cool, whatever the situation. You can trust him and he's always on the side of justice. He's strong and fit so can keep up the pace (and believe me, I'm fast!) when we're on the run. Barry is one of life's good guys and a true friend - just don't tease him about donuts, he's a bit sensitive if you mention them!

Notes: Top cop, keen sense of justice

loyal

Will fight for people's rights

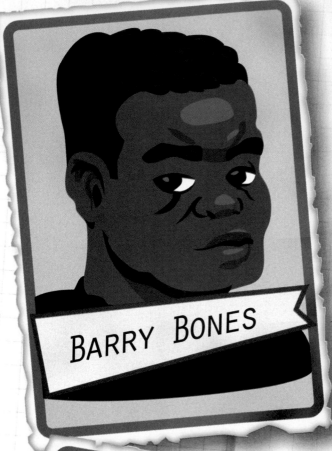

BARRY BONES

#3 TEMPLE RUN

UNLOCK:
Collect 25,000 coins

ABILITIES:
· Fighting crime
· Calm in a crisis
· Strong and agile

DISLIKES:
· Running out of donuts
· Jets of fire
· Criminals (watch out baddies!)

POWER UP:
· Coin bonus – collect an instant 50 coin bonus

FIND THE DONUTS!

Guy Dangerous did say not to mention the D-O-N-U-T-S in front of Barry, but there are 10 sugary, delicious 'unmentionables' hidden in this scene, and Barry is rather hungry! Help him find all 10, and he's sure to share them with you.

if you found all the Donuts!

COLLECT

25,000 COINS

THE CURSE OF THE IDOL!

If you're on an adventure with this explorer, don't worry if you get lost because this dude knows how to survive in the wild for months at a time...

_____

Unscramble these letters to collect this heavenly ring artifact...

NLGEA SGWNI   _ _ _ _ _ _ _ _ _

Which zip-wire will lead Francisco Montoya to the mine shaft entrance?

Barry Bones has reached the temple. But before he can grab the golden idol and run, he has to activate the magic gems in each temple chamber in order to banish the curse of the idol. Solve the clues by each pile of gems before Barry is visited by a plague of locust, or something worse! Give yourself 1000 gems if you can save Barry from a fate worse than THE CURSE OF THE IDOL! And then, RUN!

Guy Dangerous finds 467 gems. He drops 133 over a cliff edge while running from a demon monkey. He gives 250 to Scarlett Fox because, well, just because he REALLY likes her! How many gems does he have left for himself?

Help Karma Lee work out the missing number of coins in this sequence...

250 coins; ____ coins; 310 coins; 340 coins; ____ coins; ____ coins; 430 coins; ____ coins; 490 coins.

Chilling words that no explorer wants to hear! Fill in the missing word, then RUN as fast as your legs will take you!

"I eat _____ like you for breakfast."

25

COUNT THE DEMON MONKEYS

If this was a team of footballers, Zack Wonder could easily plough his way through them. But the tough big guy doesn't want to go anywhere near this gruesome demonic crowd — with good reason! Help Zack speedily count how many demon monkeys are blocking his escape, and then, yes, you know the routine, RUN! Don't bother screaming, 'cos no one will hear you over the deathly screeches of these evil creatures!

DRAW A DEMON MONKEY

The demon monkeys are truly the stuff of your worst nightmares. Don't be embarrassed — you don't have to be brave when facing (or rather running from) these hideous creatures — even Guy Dangerous is scared of them (just don't mention that in front of Scarlett Fox)!

Wow that's Scary!

COLLECT

500 COINS

WOW! THAT IS ONE S-C-A-R-Y CREATURE!

Get creative and design your own demonic creature — the scarier the better! Just remember to tell Guy and the other explorers, so they know what to run from! (Note to Guy D: We're sure Scarlett will understand your fear of this gruesome creature!)

TEMPLE RUN CHALLENGE!

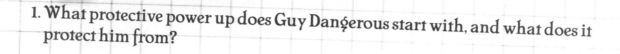

So you want to join Guy Dangerous on his next quest? You've got all the latest explorer's kit, but have you got what it takes to be a true adventurer? Guy Dangerous has set you a little test to see if you're a natural or whether you'll fall at the first obstacle. Take his quiz to see if you are up to a Temple Run challenge!

1. What protective power up does Guy Dangerous start with, and what does it protect him from?

_____

2. How many coins do you need to collect to unlock Karma Lee?

_____

3. What does a score bonus power up instantly give you?

_____

4. What country does the crafty Francisco Montoya come from?

_____

5. What precious circular artifact can you collect on your run. How many are there to collect?

_____

6. What muddy, misty place does Scarlett Fox try to avoid?

_____

7. Who has a fantastic knowledge of nature and wildlife?

_____

8. What two creatures does Karma Lee really dislike (not including all of the demon monkeys!)?

_____

9. Name the s-s-s-slithery grinning mask artifact.

_____

10. Draw the iconic Temple Run symbol.

Dude, great score!

Pack your bags, you're coming on my next quest! As you're such an intrepid explorer give yourself a boost power up and a pick up spawn ability.

SCARLETT'S SPARKLING SUDOKU

All great explorers need to have their wits about them and be able to get themselves out of sticky situations. Scarlett Fox has these qualities in abundance. Take a run with this foxy lady and see how she uses her razor sharp instincts. If you can complete this tricky picture Sudoku puzzle you might just prove yourself to be a worthy match for Scarlett. Collect a coin magnet power-up and 10,000 coins, and get planning your next adventure with Scarlett as your partner!

Well Done!

COLLECT 10,000 COINS

(Clue: Remember, each of the six images must only appear once on each horizontal and vertical line.

LOST LOOT!

Last month, Guy Dangerous decided to stash some of his treasures in an old abandoned mine shaft. He'd managed to collect so many artifacts, gems, coins and an idol or two, on his last few quests, and he didn't want to carry them on his next mission — it's hard to run from those evil demon monkeys if you are weighted down with a big sack of treasures!

The only trouble is, now that Guy's gone back to the mine to collect his loot, he can't quite remember where he hid it all! Help him locate all the items (luckily Guy listed all the treasures he had collected in his journal!) and he promises to give you one of his golden idols, a travelling tiki mask and a bag of 1,000 coins. BONUS! That's easier than having to RUN for them!

if you found all the Objects
COLLECT
1000 COINS

4x

3x

1x

8x

3x

30

MEET SCARLETT FOX

Where can I start with Scarlett? She is one cool lady - always in control and she never let's her guard down even in the face of danger. She has a talent for getting out of tricky situations, which is handy when you're on a quest for treasure and you some how find yourself trapped on a crumbling narrow ledge! She's an ideal adventure partner because she has razor sharp instincts, always goes for her goal and is a great long distance runner. She's super organized, and even though I hate to admit to it, she's a natural leader. One word of warning though- watch out for that fiery temper of hers - she can cut you down with her words and quick wit.

Notes: **Determined**
Can-do attitude
Cunning
Organized, sharp-witted
Fiery

SCARLETT FOX

#4 TEMPLE RUN

UNLOCK:
Collect 5,000 coins

ABILITIES:
· Natural leader
· Long-distance running
· Combat fighting

DISLIKES:
· Swamps
· Piranhas
· Sharp turns

POWER UP:
· Boost forward

CROCODILE SWAMP!

The fiery Scarlett isn't scared of much, but there are some things she dislikes even more than Guy's bad jokes! To reach the temple she's got to face her fears and cross a misty piranha-infested swamp. If you dare, help poor Scarlett find her way through the razor-toothed nightmare before her!

If you help Scarlett cross the swamp!

COLLECT

5,000 COINS

START

PARTY TEMPLE RUN STYLE!

It's time to take off your running shoes and PARTAY! Just make sure the demon monkeys don't get wind of it and crash the fun! You've already got an awesome theme — Temple Run explorers — so here's what you need to do to get this party up and RUNNING!

PARTY TO DO LIST

- ☐ Make invites
- ☐ Make decorations
- ☐ Ideas for party food (lots of cakes!)
- ☐ Ideas for games to play
- ☐ Party bags

INVITES

Decide on a date, time and venue for your party and then send out your cool Temple Run invites. Don't forget to invite Guy Dangerous and his friends or the curse of the golden idol might befall you!

INVITATIONS

Use this template to make as many invites as you need, or get super creative and design some of your own. You can decorate them with all the different Temple Run symbols, objects and artifacts. Flick through the pages of this book to get inspired.

INVITATION

You are invited to

An Awesome

TEMPLE RUN

Themed Party!

ARE YOU UP FOR THE CHALLENGE?

Date:

_____

Time:

_____

Venue:

_____

_____

RSVP

to accept this quest.

DANGEROUS DECORATIONS!

Once you've sorted the venue for your party, it's time to think about making some cool decorations to create a real Temple Run atmosphere. Here are some ideas to get you started.

POSTERS

Stick the awesome posters from this Annual on the wall of your party room.

EXPLORER BALLOONS

Blow up a balloon for each of your friends coming to the party, and decorate them with their favourite Temple Run character. Using images from the internet or photocopied from this book, cut out the characters and stick one on each balloon. Don't forget to decorate a balloon for yourself. Which character will you choose?

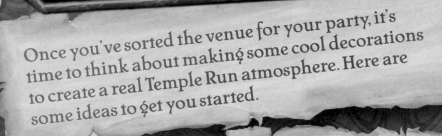

ANCIENT TEMPLE

If you're feeling really creative, you could draw brick patterns, with cracks and mossy patches on large sheets of paper, and stick them one the walls to make your party room look like the insides of an ancient temple. TERRIFIC!

BARRY BONE'S BANNERS AND BUNTING

Banners and bunting will transform your party venue. If Barry Bones was hosting the party he would certainly have them (along with a huge plate of donuts!).
To make a banner, get a large sheet of paper (or stick several sheets together with sticky tape) and then draw, write or stick images of Temple Run characters, icons and words on it. You could have a banner saying, "Enter the temple if you dare!", or "Run for your life!", or one saying, "Feeding time!" near the party food.

IN THE DARK!

Give all your guests a small torch and turn the lights low to add an extra mysterious atmosphere to your TR party. Just watch out that a demon monkey doesn't creep up in the dark and get you or your pals!

For your cool explorer's bunting, first get a piece of string or ribbon long enough to reach across the area you want to decorate. Cut out enough large triangles from coloured card, to fill the length of your string or ribbon. Decorate each triangle with drawings or cut out pictures of the intrepid TR explorers, the gruesome demon monkeys or lots of different TR icons and patterns. You could decorate one string of bunting with images of coins and gems to add some sparkle to your Temple venue, or perhaps you could have a running figure on each triangle, to make it look like someone is running around the room!

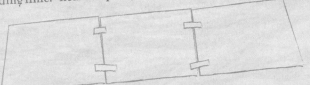

FANTASTIC FEAST!

It's feeding time! After all that running, you intrepid adventurers need to eat to get your energy back! Fill your party table with a fabulous feast of TR-themed sandwiches, fruits and nuts and cakes!

Explorers on the run would eat grapes, exotic fruits, nuts and seeds that they find in the forests and jungles. Fill a bowl with colourful, juicy fruits, and some little bowls with a variety of nuts and seeds. YUMMY and great for restoring energy!

If you're feeling really adventurous, make some cupcake wrappers to give your cakes a Temple Run touch, using the template printed on this page.

Trace the template, stick it on to thin card and cut it out. Use the template to make as many cake wrappers as you need.

Decorate each wrapper by drawing or sticking Temple Run images on them.

Finally, fold the wrapper around your cupcake case and stick the ends together with sticky tape.

Ice your cupcakes with TR symbols using different coloured icing pen tubes.

Make TR cocktail sticks to decorate your sandwiches, sausages, pizza slices and cakes. Cut out several small head shots of each of the explorers and demon monkeys and stick them on small coin or gem-shaped pieces of coloured card. Next stick each 'head' to a cocktail stick with sticky tape. You could also write what the food is under the images — for example, Karma Lee's tasty cheese, Dangerous Tuna surprise, Scarlett's scotch egg, Francisco's fairy cake, Barry Bones' delicious donuts, Demon Monkey margherita slice. Finally, place the decorated cocktail sticks in your party food. What a fantastic feast fit for hungry explorers!

GUY'S GAMES

All awesome parties need to have a few cool games to make them go with a real swing! You could use the quizzes, puzzles and board game in this book to get you started

Find the idol

Find the idol is another fun game to play. Draw or cut out several images of the golden idol and take it in turns to hide them. Everyone else then goes on a 'quest' to find as many idols as possible in a set amount of time. Whoever finds the most idols in the time allowed, is the winner!

Demon Monkey catch

If you've got some outside space available at your party, why not have some running races, to see who is the fastest Temple Run explorer. You could also play Demon Monkey catch. Choose someone to be the Demon Monkey. Designate a place in the garden to be the 'safe home base'. The Demon Monkey counts to 20 while all the other 'explorer's run around the garden, and then they have to try and catch as many explorers in a set time limit of 5 minutes. The explorers can run to the safe base, but they can't stay on it for more than a minute. RUN for your life and watch out for those sharp claws!

Temple Run snap

If you're feeling up to the challenge, make your own Temple Run snap cards. Cut out 40 same-sized rectangles from thin card to make your cards. Draw or stick images of the explorers, Demon Monkeys, gems, coins or the idol on the cards. You will need to create two cards of each design.

To play the game, shuffle the pack of cards and place them face down on a table or the floor. Take it in turns to turn two cards over to try and find the matching pairs. The winner is the person with the most matching pairs when there are no cards left. To make the game trickier, you could use the Demon Monkey cards to get people out of the game. If someone picks up a Demon Monkey, they are out of the game. Players still in the game, count up their matching pairs when only the two Demon Monkey cards are left on the table. The winner is the person with the most matching pairs.

ADVENTURER'S ANCIENT ARTIFACT

Finding an ancient artifact on a treasure hunt expedition gives you a great feeling. Guy Dangerous is desperately trying to collect all 10 ancient rings and mask artifacts, so that he can impress Scarlett Fox with his collection (maybe then she'll take him a bit more seriously!).

Before you set off on your next adventure with Guy Dangerous, to help him try to complete his artifact stash, get creative and design your own ancient artifact here. Give it a name and list all the types explorers will need to search for on their next mission. Get drawing and then RUN!

Zack is one big, cool dude! You should see him play American football, I feel sorry for the opposition. Poor Zack somehow found himself transported into my crazy world of adventure and treasure seeking, when he accidentally got hold of the ultimate treasure, the golden idol. His agility, brute force and speed on the pitch have proved to be the perfect skills for an intrepid explorer! Apart from his fear of mine shafts (can't say I blame him, they're not somewhere you want to be stuck for long) and things with large teeth, Zack is just the kinda guy you want to have with you when you're battling demon monkeys. And boy can he RUN!

Notes:

Elusive

American football star

Nimble

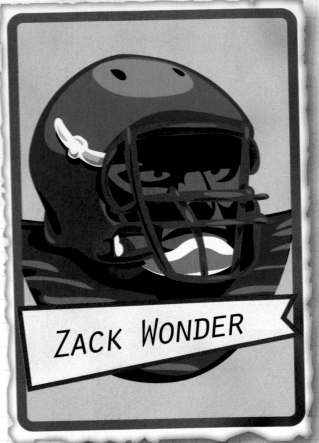

ZACK WONDER

#5 TEMPLE RUN

UNLOCK:
Collect 250,000 coins

ABILITIES:
· Super fit and strong
· Fast and agile
· Brute force

DISLIKES:
· Other football teams when they win
· Mine shafts

DEMONIC FOOTBALL KIT

Football and exploring are two of Zack Wonder's favourite activities. If only he could combine them both! Imagine Zack and his football buddies taking on a team of demon monkeys on the pitch, awesome! Design a football kit fit for a gruesome demon monkey to wear!

for coming up with a cool demon design!

COLLECT

25,000 COINS

KEEP ON RUNNING!

Keep on running! Guy, Barry and Scarlett have all set out on a new quest. They are all determined to reach the temple and the golden idol first.) Can they find the shortest route and save themselves some time? The stakes are high, because whichever explorer takes the longest to complete the run, they have to give the other two explorers 500 gold coins and 50 gems each, and you 1000 coins and a gem bonus power-up! Dude, get calculating from the clues below, which intrepid explorer out-runs the others! My money's on the foxy lady!

(especially Ms FOX who always has to be the WINNER!)

Watch him go! Guy Dangerous is off the starting block like a bullet out of a gun. He uses his Mega Head Start, which boosts him 2,500m. His stopwatch says only 10 seconds have passed. Over the next 3 minutes he travels another 5,000m, successfully dodging obstacles and managing not to fall off the narrow cliff ledges! Up ahead Guy sees rapids. He takes 30 seconds to cover the 500m to reach them and then stops to work out how he can get across. Two minutes tick by while he searches for a way across. Then, he spies a handy vine hanging from the edge of the cliff. He grabs it and swings himself across the 50m rapids ravine, in a record-breaking speed of 10 seconds. It takes Guy 30 seconds to get his bearings and then he runs another 10,000m without tripping. This takes him 8 minutes. The temple looms in the distance — 20,000m away. Guy Dangerous takes another 15 minutes to reach it, but he falls on the way and has to add a 5 minute time penalty. He also uses his shield power up twice, which adds another 7 minute time penalty. He finally reaches the temple, avoiding the grasping claws of a Demon Monkey and grabs the idol before starting his run back home. Well done Guy Dangerous! Take 3 minutes off your final time for avoiding the gruesome creature!

Scarlett Fox is focused and ready to run off the competition (especially that smug Guy Dangerous!). She is super organised and has already prepared various power-ups in case she needs a boost. Using a Head Start boost, Scarlett races 2,000m along the narrow path in 5 seconds. She speeds along another 3,000m in 6 minutes, leaping over several crumbling walls on the way and narrowly avoiding four jets of fire, earning back 2 minutes time bonus, but then, Disaster strikes! Poor Scarlett. A minute later she hits a sharp bend another 1,000m on, as a huge demon monkey jumps out at her. She is going too fast and as she swerves to avoid the beast she falls off the cliff edge! Quick as a flash, she uses a Save Me, so she can continue the race, so she can continue the race, but that's cost her 10 minutes to be added to her final time. Not to be deterred, this fiery lady picks herself up and races off, covering 5,000m in 8 minutes, her long distance running skills coming into their own. She quickly gains back a 5 minute time bonus as she skillfully maneuvers around a waterfall and rides the rapids, taking her 2,000m in 2 minutes to the edge of a forest. She can see the temple 1,000m away, but she has got to face her worst fear and get across a piranha-infested swamp to reach the temple entrance! She stops for 3 minutes, searching for a route across or around the swamp. Finally, she spies a zip wire high up in the trees, leading straight to the temple. It takes her a minute to climb the tree, and another 30 seconds to whizz across the steaming swamp (much to her great relief!), and with a graceful jump, land at the temple entrance and grab the golden idol. Well done, foxy lady! Take 2 minutes off your time for facing your fear!

Oh no, Barry! What are you doing? The big guy has stopped running after 500m (and 15 seconds on the clock) to pick up something on the path. What the? He's eating donuts! No, dude! Bet Ms Fox left them there to slow him down, and it's worked! Barry, that's a 10 minute time penalty for being so easily tricked! OK, he's finished eating, and is running like crazy now to try and make up time. Woah! He's fast! He's travelled the next 2,500m in 4 and half minutes flat, while avoiding jets of fire, jumping a ravine and taking a sharp turn without even sliding. That deserves a 6 minute time off his final score! Barry runs the next 5,000m without tripping, in 10 minutes. He stops for 1 minute to use his coin magnet power-up, and this costs him a 2 minute time penalty. He can see the temple over the tops of the trees, but he's got to get through a mine shaft first to reach it. He jumps in an abandoned mine cart and whizzes through the mine shaft in 8 minutes. The mine tracks carry him over 10,000m. A minute later and 500m on, Mr Bones reaches the temple and grabs the golden idol. Well done, sir! Give yourself a 5 minute time bonus off your final score just because you didn't encounter any Demon Monkeys on your route.

SCOREBOARD

Guy Dangerous   ran ___m in ___minutes and ___seconds.
Barry Bones   ran ___m in ___minutes and ___seconds.
Scarlett Fox   ran ___m in ___minutes and ___seconds.

The WINNER is _____! Awesome!

Could you beat the winner's time?
COLLECT
1000 COINS

45

MONTOYA'S MAGNIFICENT MONEY TIN!

If there's one thing that the wily, smooth-talking Francisco Montoya loves even more than women, it's treasure — gems, artifacts, and especially gold coins! But he really hates losing it or having it pinched while he is on another gold-seeking quest. Help the old conquistador keep his stash safe, by making this awesome silver money tin for him to store all his coins.

You will need:
- A helpful adult
- Access to a photocopier or scanner
- Sturdy card
- Scissors
- Glue

1. With the help of an adult, photocopy or scan the lid, base and divider templates on pages 47, 48 and 49.

2. Stick each template on the card and carefully cut them out, using the dotted lines as guides.

3. Fold each tin 'part' along the lines indicated.

4. Glue the lid together using the tabs as indicated. Press firmly to make sure it is properly stuck together and leave to dry.

5. Next glue the base together using the tabs as indicated. Press firmly to make sure it is properly stuck together and leave to dry.

6. Cut the slots in the divider pieces as indicated, and slot them together. Put the completed divider in the base of the money tin, to create compartments for all of Montoya's money.

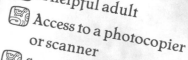
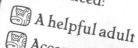
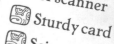

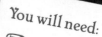

Cut along these lines

Fold along these lines

glue

glue

glue

glue

glue Lid to base

glue

glue

glue

glue

HANDS OFF!

DRAW YOUR OWN TEMPLE RUN TERRAIN!

A true explorer has to learn to cope with all sorts of environments and terrains on a quest, and has to be prepared for whatever nature throws at them — rapids, dense forests, damp swamps, sheer cliff drops, creepy caves, and the odd Demon Monkey or two! If you're a natural like Montana Smith, then nowhere is too difficult a challenge. This dude can survive in the wild, with only his compass, for weeks at a time — truly awe-inspiring!

Grab a pencil and get designing your own new Temple Run environment. It can be anything you can imagine. Do you think Guy Dangerous and his fellow explorers could survive a run through this new place? They might need to ask Montana for some help!

What a creepy, cool place! Dude, give yourself 3 golden idols for your awesome efforts!

CRACK THE CODE!

Scarlett Fox needs to enlist Guy Dangerous' help on her next quest, although she hates to admit it! She needs to find an archaeologist, who has mysteriously disappeared in the jungle after stumbling upon a new golden idol and an ancient temple that holds the clues to some centuries-old buried treasure. The mission is top secret. Scarlett doesn't want any information to fall into the wrong hands, so she has written Guy Dangerous a message in code.

Using the coded alphabet, help Guy decipher Scarlett's message. Maybe they'll let you go on this adventure with them! Collect a twisted root ring artifact for showing such sharp explorer skills!

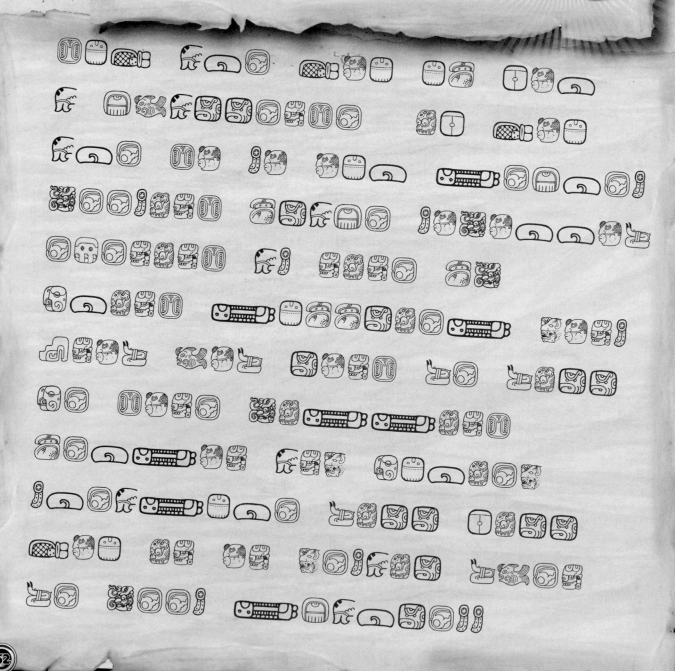

WHICH EXPLORER ARE YOU?

You've proved yourself to be a brave and intrepid explorer, but which of the Temple Run explorer heroes are you most like? Can you swing on a vine or run for long distances? Can you survive in the wild, or kick some serious butt with your martial skills? Do you have brute force or are you calm in a crisis? Is your love of gold greater than anything? Take this quick test to find out who you most resemble. You might be in for a surprise! Let's hope it's a pleasant one!

1. You've just heard about a new treasure to be found in an ancient temple. What do you do to prepare for your quest?

A. Rush out to buy hair gel supplies – you want to look your best just in case you should bump into a certain someone!

B. Get practising some new martial art moves, and do a few cryptic crosswords to keep the old grey matter ticking over.

C. Check out the crime rates for the country you are going to be travelling in, and then chill out in front of the TV with a box of donuts!

D. Pack your rucksack, making sure you've got all the things you might need in an emergency, and then spend some time studying a map of the area the quest will take you through.

E. Ring the coach to tell him you're going to be away for a while, and then arrange one last football game before you go.

F. Clean and pack your weapons, and a compass, and then go to your favourite saloon for a drink.

G. Polish your armour and dream of how much treasure you are going to find (and ways in which you can keep more than your fair share!).

H. "Mmmm, more crispy explorers!"

2. You're racing along a narrow cliff ledge, when suddenly a Demon Monkey jumps out at you. What do you do?

A. Search for a vine to make a quick escape, while staying close to the cliff wall so you don't have to look over the edge and see how far the drop is – eeeeek!

B. Try to reason with the hideous creature before kicking its butt!

C. Throw some donuts to it to distract it, and then run as fast as you can.

D. Jump off the ledge and use one of your Save Me chances.

E. Charge straight at the beast and knock it over the cliff edge.

F. Wrestle it to the ground, while slyly pulling out one of your weapons from your leather pouch.

G. Turn on your charm – it works with the ladies, and it just might save you this time!

H. Grunt "hello!" and join in the fun!

3. You are a brave explorer, but even you have some things you just don't like (just don't tell the others!).

A. Clifftop walkways.
B. Snakes and crocodiles.
C. Jets of fire.
D. Piranhas.
E. Mine shafts.
F. Dark temples.
G. Zip-lines.
H. Everything!

4. You come to the edge of a misty, muddy swamp. How do you plan to get round it?

A. Climb a tree and swing across it on a handy vine.

B. Looking out for snakes and crocodiles, you leap from tree branch to branch and somersault to the ground on the other side.

C. You use your strength and agility to climb through the trees until you reach dry ground again.

D. You hate swamps and this is your worst nightmare. You take a few deep breaths and then look for an alternative route.

E. You use your brute strength to push down a tree, so you can use it to cross the swamp.

F. Using your compass, you work out a new route to avoid having to cross the swamp.

G. Take off your armour so it doesn't get dirty, and then construct a small boat out of branches and vines and row across the swamp.

H. Look out for something tasty to eat in all that lovely mud!

5. You reach the temple and grab the idol. But then you hear one of your fellow explorers calling out for help. What do you do?

A. Drop the idol and go to help – it could be your favourite person, and you definitely want to impress her by saving her!

B. Hide the idol somewhere safe, and then, albeit reluctantly, go to their aid.

C. Your friends are more important than any treasure – forget the idol and rush to help them.

D. Tuck the idol under your belt, and calmly use your razor-sharp wits to work out a plan to help them.

E. Abandon the treasure hunt and rush to help – you didn't really want to be there anyway.

F. Although you are a loner, you can't just walk away from a fellow explorer, so you go to help. You can always find another idol anyway!

G. The idol is gold, you just can't leave it! Ignore the cries for help and run off to add your treasure to your growing stash!

H. Go to find the explorer because you are very hungry!

MOSTLY As
You're like Guy Dangerous.

MOSTLY Bs
You're like Karma Lee.

MOSTLY Cs
You're like Barry Bones.

MOSTLY Ds
You're like Scarlett Fox.

MOSTLY Es
You're like Zack Wonder.

MOSTLY Fs
You're like Montana Smith.

MOSTLY Gs
You're like Francisco Montoya.

MOSTLY Hs
Eeeeek! Either you've got a warped sense of humour or you're a demon monkey in disguise!

I was sitting in a quiet saloon when I met Montana. I think he overheard me talking to the barman about my latest quest. In a gravelly voice asked me if I was a treasure hunter. I was a bit suspicious of him at first - he looked rough and dangerous, with his hat pulled down over his eyes. He started telling me about this strange idol he was seeking and the evil-looking creatures that guarded it. Turns out we are searching for the same thing! He said he usually worked alone, but he would join me and help. Don't know whether to trust him or not, but he is an expert tracker and survivor in the wild, so he will be a very useful guide through the swamps and jungles.

Notes: In touch with nature,

loner
expert explorer

Outlaw of the wild west   survivor

MONTANA SMITH

#6 TEMPLE RUN

UNLOCK:
Collect 250,000 coins

ABILITIES:
· Great knowledge and experience of nature
· Not afraid to wrestle troublesome beasts
· Skilled with weapons

DISLIKES:
· Dark temples
· City folk
· Washing
· Not being near a saloon

MATCH THE TRACKS

This lone adventurer really knows his nature and wildlife (and come to think of it, he does have a rather musty animal like smell about him!). If you want to find out which animals made these footprints, then you'd better try and persuade Montana Smith to join you on your quest. Maybe a bag-full of gems might do the job?

if your tracking skills are up to scratch!
COLLECT 500 GEMS

Tiger

Elephant

Orangutan

Lion

Giraffe

Penguin

QUEST FOR THE LOST TREASURE

Clues

Write down the map grid coordinates for each clue to help you solve this mystery!

1. Find the figure of eight temple symbol carved into the rocks (Grid ____:____)

2. Look for the forked tree by the lagoon (Grid ____:____)

3. There are 3 rocks in the rapids, go to the smallest one. (Grid ____:____)

4. Watch out for the hideous Demon Monkey – hide in the mine shaft behind the cart that has 6 gems in it. (Grid ____:____)

5. You've reached the murky swamp. Find the small boat hidden in the bushes to cross it. Avoid the piranhas at all costs! (Grid ____:____)

6. You've reached the temple. Find the idol mask. (Grid ____:____)

Take the horizontal grid number from clue 1 and multiply it by 2.
Take the vertical grid number from clue 6 and add 5 to it.

The treasure is buried at: (Grid ____:____)

Montana Smith has found a lost diary hidden in an old rotten tree trunk. It looks like it must have once belonged to another explorer, and stuck between the pages is a treasure map. Montana can't believe his luck! Help him work out the clues written on the map. Once you locate the treasure, he promises to give you 1,000 coins and 500 gems. Happy hunting!

ZAP NOW!

My dear new adventure partners, I know how brave you already are and what excellent explorers you are going to make, but I am going to have to tell you something that you are not going to like to hear. Sorry dudes! It really wouldn't be fair to keep this from you, even at the risk of turning you away. Something scary and evil lurks out there, on every quest you make. It's always there somewhere, waiting to get its hideous fangs and claws into you. You can RUN, you can HIDE, but this terrible beast will always be searching for you, and it will not stop chasing you... EVER! I am talking about the evil guardians of the idol, the Demon Monkeys (Ugh! I can hardly bear to say the name). These grotesque beasts will pursue anyone who steals the idol, and then eat them for breakfast! No obstacle is too much for them.

DEMON MONKEY

#7 TEMPLE RUN

UNLOCK: They're always behind you, chasing you!

ABILITIES:
· Screeching hideously and scraping their claws
· Chasing explorers over any distance
· Hiding the golden idol

DISLIKES:
· Everybody and everything, especially treasure hunters
· Sunlight, Happiness
· Losing the idol

IT'S FEEDING TIME!

Yikes! Run for your life! The Demon Monkeys are closing in on their prey. Which unlucky explorer is about to get caught? They might be better off throwing themselves off a cliff! Try and save them and earn yourself a golden idol.

Great Job!
GOLDEN IDOL

MAKE A DEMON MONKEY MASK!

Urgghhhh! Scary or what! If you dare, photocopy, scan or trace this hideous face, stick it on thin card and then cut it out. Secure with ribbon or string in the holes indicated. Get an adult that isn't easily frightened to help you!

Now it's ready to wear and you can chase your friends on a temple run around the garden or in the park! Can you catch them?

MAKE A DEMON MONKEY CLAW!

To complete the hideousness, why not make this Demon Monkey claw hand as well. You'll be truly grotesque and your friends will be RUNNING for their lives!

As with the mask, photocopy, scan or trace this disgusting sharp-clawed hand, stick it on thin card and then cut it out. Stick a length of ribbon on the underside of the claw (as indicated), so that you can secure it around your forearm and over your hand Eeeeek! That's scary!

WANTED!

Don't be fooled by this sweet-talking, golden-haired conquistador! He may be a hit with the ladies, but this wily, silver-tongued old devil, will lie, cheat and steal his way out of any situation. You've been warned! If you don't want your treasure to suddenly 'disappear', then keep your eyes peeled for this charming face! He goes by the name of Francisco Montoya (great name, have to admit!).

Use the grid to copy this suave picture of Señor Montoya in all his armoured glory. You won't forget this face in a hurry!

Give yourself a Skyward Scream mask artifact for your splendido effort!

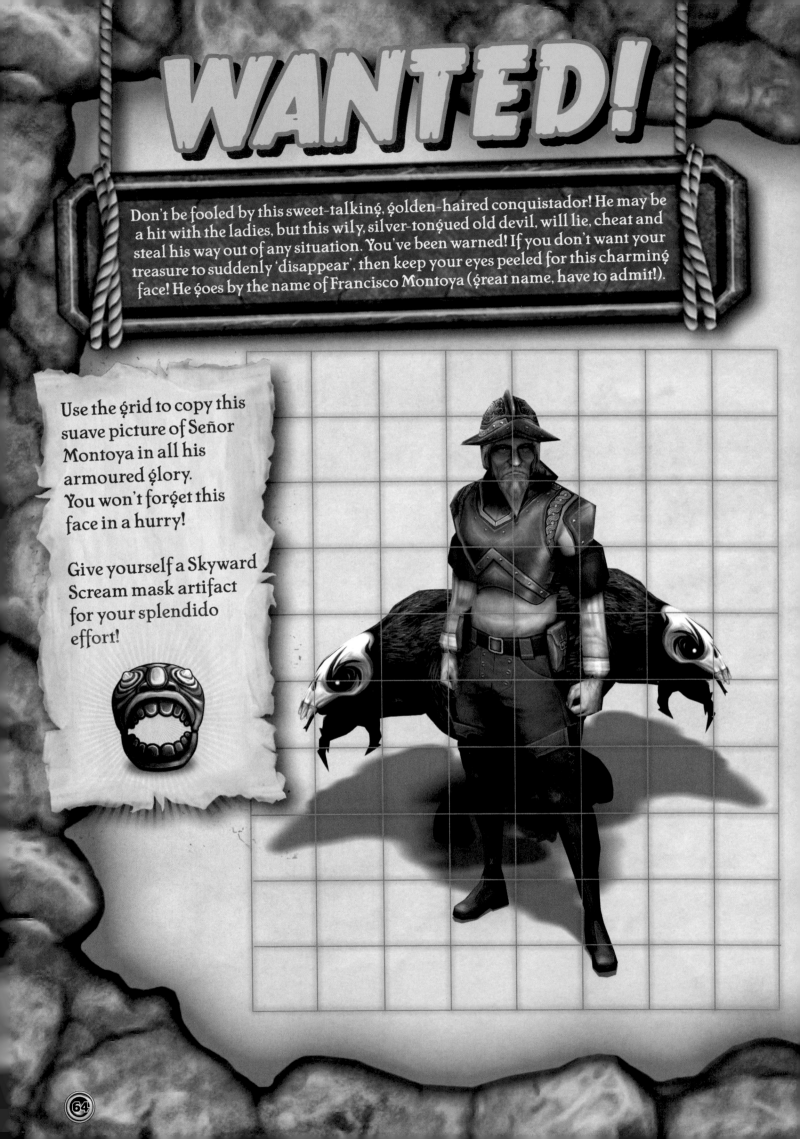

There is nothing nice about this man at all – he lies, cheats and steals, and will turn against you the minute you let down your guard. The ladies might be fooled by his polished suit of armour and Spanish charm, but I am definitely not! I don't like his sneaky manner. And for one thing, he's going to be way too hot in the jungle in that get up of his! I'm going to try and lose him as soon as I can. I do not want him taking over my quest.

FRANCISCO MONTOYA

Notes:

Thief
Cheater, liar
obsessed with gold
crafty
Spanish conquistador

#8 TEMPLE RUN

UNLOCK:
Collect 100,000 coins

ABILITIES:
· Debonair, charming, smooth talker with the ladies
· Experienced explorer
· Ruthless not afraid to do whatever it takes to get what he wants

DISLIKES:
· Zip-lines
· Scratching his armour
· Honesty
· Losing treasure, especially gold

COUNT THE COINS

All that glitters is... GOLD! This crafty explorer will take on any quest, just to get his armour-clad hands on the gold stuff! In fact any treasure (the glittery and shinier the better) will do. Can you help Francisco Montoya count how many coins and gems he has stashed away?

to add to Francisco's treasure pile if you get your sums right.

COLLECT

100,000 COINS

Totals

Coins

Gemstones

SPOT THE SECRET SEQUENCE

Francisco Montoya loves gold more than he really should! He's found a secret vault in an ancient tomb that is rumoured to hold an old diary that belonged to a treasure hunter, and written in it is the secret location to all his worldly treasures! The only trouble is, that to open the vault, he's got to identify the key sequence of four ancient symbols, that appear only once in the grid pattern carved into the crumbling walls.

If you feel like helping this old thief spot the sequence (although don't blame you if you don't want to), then there are 2 ring artifacts in it for you — the infinite loop and the mystic rocks.

SHARP EYED EXPLORER!

An explorer needs to keep their wits about them all the time. They need to have sharp instincts and a keen sense of observation. Karma Lee is always alert and aware of her surroundings. Can you match her skills. Take a good look at this scene for about a minute, then turn the page and see how observant you really are by answering the questions.

Are you the sort of explorer that Karma Lee would happily take with her on a treasure seeking adventure?

ZAP NOW!

KARMA'S MEMORY TEST

Are you a sharp-eyed explorer? Answer these questions to see if you meet the grade. Karma Lee got 10 out of 10 by the way — no pressure, dude!

1. How many ancient face symbols are carved into the rocks near the entrance to the temple?

_____

2. Which explorer is wearing a blue top?

_____

3. How many gem rocks are hanging from the top of the temple's entrance?

_____

4. Name the two objects sitting on the figure of 8 symbol carved into the ground.

_____

5. What demonic thing is creeping into the left hand side of the picture?

_____

6. How many objects are there in total in front of the temple entrance?

_____

7. Which explorer is standing on the left hand side?

_____

8. How many figure of 8 symbols did you see in the scene?

_____

9. What colour is the gem to the right of the red spiky ring?

_____

10. What colour is Karma Lee's headband?

_____

WHO'S BEHIND YOU?

Guy Dangerous has an uneasy feeling. He's been running flat out for the last 5,000 m, he's avoided all sorts of obstacles, jumped a ravine, slid down the rapids and picked up 800 coins. But out of the corner of his eye he keeps catching a sinister shadowy figure. He stops to catch his breath. There is a rustling sound back along the narrow path. Who or what is lurking in the bushes? It doesn't seem like a Demon Monkey — they're usually keen to announce their arrival with an ear-piercing screech!

Wow, That's Scary! COLLECT 500 GEMS

If you dare, go and investigate to see who or what is following Guy Dangerous. Draw your findings here, and award yourself 500 gems for your bravery!

ADVENTURE TIME!

Join Guy Dangerous and his fellow explorers on another exciting adventure! Can you help them complete their temple run safely (without being caught by those pesky demonic creatures!) and collect as many coins and gems on the way? All you need is a dice, some counters, this game board and some friends to play with.

On your marks, get set, RUN! If you land on the start of a vine or a zip-wire, follow it up to the square where it ends. If you land on a mine cart track, follow it back down to its end. Sorry dudes! But hey, no adventure is complete without a few challenges.

The winner is the person to complete the run the fastest. Happy running! You can also play this game with the winner being the person who has collected the most coins and gems on route. You might want to set a time limit in this version of the game.

START

Pick up a ring artifact. Move 2 spaces forward.

Coin bonus: collect 500 coins

Nearly caught by a Demon Monkey. Miss a turn.

If you're feeling really adventurous, make your own awesome TR spinner and counters, using the templates on this page. Photocopy, scan or trace the templates, stick them on thin card, and cut out (ask an adult to help you with this). To make the spinner clue on card and put a cocktail stick through the centre.

Use a mega head start, move forward 4 spaces

Gem bonus: collect 50 gems

GO TO NEXT PAGE

Take a sharp bend too fast. Go back 8 spaces

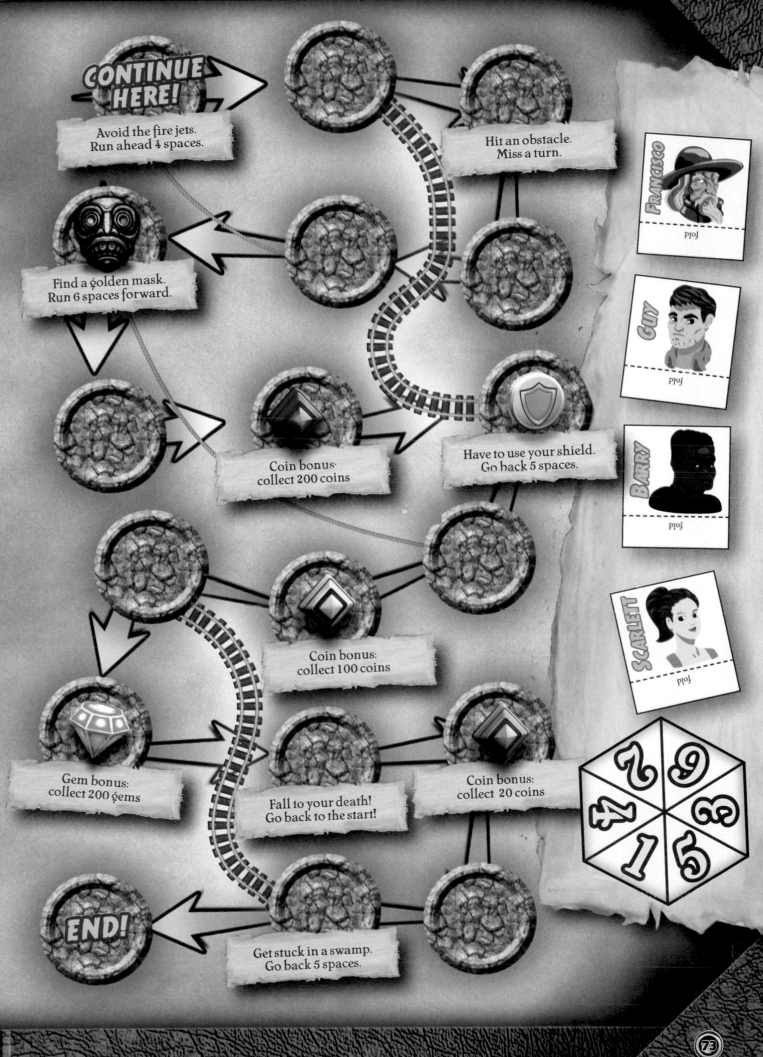

CONTINUE HERE!

Avoid the fire jets.
Run ahead 4 spaces.

Hit an obstacle.
Miss a turn.

Find a golden mask.
Run 6 spaces forward.

Coin bonus:
collect 200 coins

Have to use your shield.
Go back 5 spaces.

Coin bonus:
collect 100 coins

Gem bonus:
collect 200 gems

Fall to your death!
Go back to the start!

Coin bonus:
collect 20 coins

END!

Get stuck in a swamp.
Go back 5 spaces.

Francisco
fold

Guy
fold

Barry
fold

Scarlett
fold

73

You've met, and seen in action, Guy Dangerous and his fellow intrepid adventurers. They're a pretty impressive bunch overall, each bringing individual skills to every treasure hunt. But they could always use some extra help in their never-ending quest for the golden idol.

Design and draw your own new explorer to join their team. What abilities do they have that will make them a great adventurer? What do they like and dislike? What's their power-up and how do you 'unlock' them?

#13 TEMPLE RUN

UNLOCK:

ABILITIES:

DISLIKES:

POWER UP:

Collect a
Ring of your Choice
COLLECT

RING ARTEFACT

I'm liking what I see.
This explorer is fast on
their feet and a quick
thinker. I think I'll ask
them to come on my
next adventure.

Well done, awesome adventurer! You dodged the dangers and took on the challenges. Keep on RUNNING! and see ya on my next quest!
-Guy Dangerous!

QUEST SCORECARD

POINTS:

ABILITIES:

POWER UPS:

COINS:

GEMS:

ARTIFACTS:

GOLDEN IDOLS:

THERE ARE _____. RUNNING EXPLORERS IN THIS COOL ANNUAL!

ANSWERS

Page 7
Vine 4

Page 15
1. 8.02am
2. 247 coins; 135 gems
3. 9 artifacts each
4. 469 coins
5. 100 gems

Page 16

Page 17

Page 20

Page 21

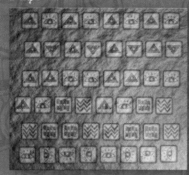

Page 23

Page 24/25
1. ANGEL WINGS;
2. Montana Smith;
3. 84 gems;
4. X;
5. explorers;
6. 280, 370, 400, 460

Page 26
29 Demon Monkeys.

Page 28
1. Shield; helps protect him from obstacles.
2. 25,000 coins
3. Collect an instant 500 point bonus
4. Spain
5. A ring. There are 10 different rings to collect.
6. A swamp
7. Montana Smith
8. Snakes and Crocodiles
9. Serpent's Smile mask
10.

Page 29

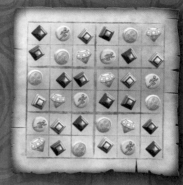

Page 30/31

Page 33

Page 44/45
SCOREBOARD
The WINNER is Scarlett Fox. Awesome!
Guy Dangerous ran: 38,000 m in 38 minutes and 20 seconds.
Barry Bones ran: 18,500 m in 25 minutes and 45 seconds.
Scarlett Fox ran: 14,000 m in 22 minutes and 35 seconds.

Page 52/53
Guy are you up for a challenge if you are go to our secret meeting place tomorow evening at nine pm bring supplies dont know how long we will be gone Missing person and buried treasure will fill you in on detail when we meet Scarlett

Page 57

Page 58/59
The treasure is buried at:
Grid (14: 10)

Page 61
Scarlett Fox

Page 67
There are 30 coins and 12 gems.

Page 68

Page 70
1. Two 2. Barry Bones
3. Four 4. Gold Idol ring Artifact and magnet coin
5. A Demon Monkey claw
6. Seven 7. Guy Dangerous
8. Two 9. Red 10. Yellow